Mr Utterson was a man of the law. He had a rugged face that was never lit by a smile. He was stern with himself, but much less so with others. Even in extreme cases he was willing to help rather than to blame.

"I am inclined to agree with **Cain** in this," was the odd way he put it. "I let my brother go to **the Devil** in his own way!"

ROBERT LOUIS STEVENSON'S

STRANGE CASE OF

Dr Jekyll and Mr Hyde

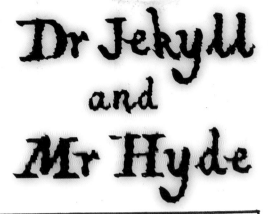

His friends were those people who were related to him, or those whom he had known the longest.

This was what bound him to **Mr Richard Enfield**, his distant cousin, the well-known man about town.

By chance on one of their Sunday walks the way led them down a side street in a busy part of London...

Adapted by
ALAN GRANT

Illustrated by
CAM KENNEDY

Coloured and lettered by
JAMIE GRANT
NIALL CONNOLLY

"Suddenly I saw two figures: one was a **little man** who was stumping along to the East at a good pace..."

"And the other a **girl** of about 8 or 10, running as hard as she could down a cross street."

"The two ran into one another at the corner."

"And then came the **horrible** part of it all..."

"The man **trampled** over the child's body and left her **screaming** on the ground!"

YOU, sir!

I hated the gentleman who had done this at first sight. So did the child's family, which was to be expected. But the doctor...

Every time he looked at my prisoner, the doctor turned **white** with the desire to **kill** him!

"I had never seen such hate in people's faces.

"And there was the man in the middle, with a kind of black, sneering calm – carrying it off, sir, just like **the Devil himself!**"

Every gentleman wants to **avoid** a **scene**. How much do you want?

We pushed the sum up to a **hundred pounds** for the child's family, and where do you think he got the money from, if not that place with the door?

He took out a key in a flash, went in and came back with 10 pounds in gold and a cheque for the rest...signed with a name I cannot say.

You never asked this... other man about the place with the door?

No, sir, I make it a rule of mine – the more it looks like **an odd sort of story**, the less I ask.

HYDE.

EDWARD HYDE.

This fellow was a really **hateful** man. But the person that made out the cheque was a good and decent man, and **famous** too.

Blackmail, I thought. An honest man paying for some of the **pranks** of his youth.

And if I do not ask **you** the name of this other, honest man, it is because I know it already. But what is the name of the man who walked over the child?

Round the corner from the by-street there was a square of very old, handsome houses...

Is **Dr Jekyll** at home, **Poole**?

My poor old Harry Jekyll! If ever I read **the Devil's mark** upon a face, it is on that of your new friend!

No, sir.

I saw Mr Hyde go in by the old **laboratory** door. Is that right?

Jekyll was wild when he was young. This Hyde must be the ghost of some old sin – he is being punished years later for things he had forgotten!

If Hyde gets the idea that there is a **will**, he may want to inherit as soon as possible.

Quite right, sir.

Mr Hyde has a key. All the servants have orders to **do what he says** – but mostly he comes and goes that way.

Poor Harry Jekyll!

Two weeks later, Dr Jekyll gave one of his enjoyable dinners to some old friends, and Mr Utterson arranged that he should stay behind at the end—

Jekyll – you know that **will** of yours..?

Utterson, I never saw a man as upset as you were by my will... unless it were that know-all, **Lanyon**, at the "nonsense" I talked about science!

You know I always thought your will was wrong. And now...I have been learning something of young **Hyde**.

What I heard was **terrible**.

I do not wish to hear more!

You do not understand my position, Utterson. I am in a painful situation.

You know I am a man to be **trusted**. Tell me the truth of this, in confidence, and I am quite sure I can get you **out** of it!

My good Utterson, I would trust you before any man in the world – even more than I trust **myself**, if I could choose.

But it is not as bad as that. Just to put your good heart at rest, I will tell you **one** thing—

12

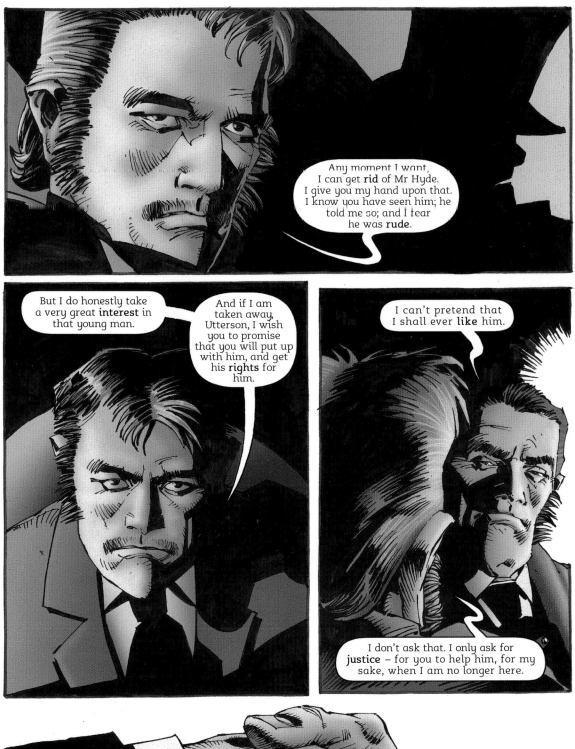

Any moment I want, I can get **rid** of Mr Hyde. I give you my hand upon that. I know you have seen him; he told me so; and I fear he was **rude**.

But I do honestly take a very great **interest** in that young man.

And if I am taken away, Utterson, I wish you to promise that you will put up with him, and get his **rights** for him.

I can't pretend that I shall ever **like** him.

I don't ask that. I only ask for **justice** – for you to help him, for my sake, when I am no longer here.

I promise.

Nearly a year later, London was startled by a very brutal crime...

A maid in a house not far from the river had gone upstairs to bed...

As she sat by her window, she became aware of a very old gentleman with white hair.

Coming to meet him was another, and very small, gentleman...

The maid was amazed to see that it was **Mr Hyde**, who had once visited her master...

Good evening, sir. May I make so bold as to ask you the way..?

All of a sudden Hyde broke out in a great fit of anger, waving his stick about and carrying on like a madman...

Next morning, Mr Utterson was called to the police station...

I am sorry to say this is **Sir Danvers Carew**, the member of Parliament! *Tut **tut**!*

The maid says that the attacker was a man called **Hyde**. An extremely **small** man – and who looked extremely **wicked**!

Aye. Edward Hyde.

The stick was broken and battered, but Utterson could see it was the one he had given many years before... to *Henry Jekyll!*

Come with me in my cab. I can take you to his house!

The first fog of the season – a great chocolate-coloured blanket – lowered over the sky as the cab crawled from street to street...

Here it would be dark, as if it were late evening. Further on there would be a glow as if some strange fire was burning...

The dismal part of Soho, seen under this swirling fog, seemed like a city in a nightmare.

16

Chapter 5: *THE LETTER*

Jekyll had bought the house from the famous surgeon. But he had changed the use of the block at the bottom of the garden...

Late in the afternoon, Utterson found his way to Jekyll's door, where a servant let him in at once...

It was the first time that Utterson had been in that part of his friend's property, and he gazed around, noting how strange and unpleasant it was...

Thank you, Poole.

You have heard the news? About **Carew**?

He was my **client**, but so are **you**; and I want to know what I am doing.

You have not been **mad** enough to take in this fellow **Hyde**?

I swear to God I will **never** set eyes on him again! I am **done** with him in this world. It is all at an end!

Indeed, he does not **want** my help. He is quite safe. Mark my words – we shall hear no more of him!

But there is one thing you could advise me about. I have been sent a **letter**, and I do not know whether I should show it to the **police**.

*The letter was written in an odd, upright hand and signed **Edward Hyde**.*

I shall keep this and sleep on it.

It said that Dr Jekyll need not be alarmed for Hyde's safety, as he had a means of escape...

Now one word more: was it **Hyde** who dictated the terms of your **will**?

The doctor nodded...

O God, what a lesson I have had!

I knew it! He was going to **murder** you. You have had a fine escape!

I have had what is far more useful. I have had a **lesson**.

By-the-by, **Poole**, someone handed in a **letter** today. What did he look like?

No letter came today, sir. Of that I am sure.

This news sent the visitor away more afraid than ever... The letter must have come to the laboratory door. It could even have been written in Jekyll's cabinet.

Special edition! Shocking murder of an M.P.!

20

Though it was his habit to be independent, Utterson began to long for some advice...

Soon, he was sitting on one side of his own fireplace with **Mr. Guest**, his head clerk, upon the other...

This man Hyde is **mad** of course!

I have a letter here in Hyde's handwriting – signed by a **murderer**!

And this is an **invitation** to dinner from Dr Jekyll.

They look oddly alike, sir. The handwriting is in many points **the same** – only the slope is different.

"What?" thought Utterson. "Would Dr Jekyll **forge** a letter for a **murderer?**"

And his blood ran cold in his veins.

Chapter 6: **THE ODD INCIDENT OF DR LANYON**

Time ran on. Thousands of pounds were offered as a reward, but Mr Hyde had vanished as if he had never existed.

WANTED FOR MURDER – –EDWARD HYDE

Tales came out telling how cruel he had been, at once so uncaring and brutal; tales of his vile life, and the hatred that followed his career...

Much of his past was revealed, and all of it was shady...

But now that this evil influence was gone, a new life began for Dr Jekyll. He had always been known for his charity work, he was now no less marked out for religion...

For two months, the doctor was at peace.

On the 8th of January, Utterson had dined at the doctor's with a small party. **Lanyon** had been there, as in the old days when the three men had been such close friends...

But on the 12th and again on the 14th, the door was shut against Utterson...

The doctor is confined to the house, sir, and is seeing no one.

Refused entry six times, Utterson went on to Doctor Lanyon's...

And was shocked at the change in the doctor. He looked close to death. He had an expression on his face that seemed to reveal that he had some deep-seated terror on his mind.

Leaving a strange letter for Utterson...

Not to be opened till the death or disappearance of Dr Henry Jekyll.

Here again was talk of another person vanishing and of it all being to do with **Jekyll**. What in the name of goodness could it all mean..?

It seems unlikely that after that day, Utterson was still keen to be with his friend Dr Jekyll.

He went to call, indeed, but he was perhaps happy when he was not allowed into that house which Jekyll had made his prison...

I fear I have no pleasant news, sir.

The doctor stays in his cabinet over the laboratory more than ever. He is depressed and has grown **silent**.

It seems as if he has something on his mind.

Mr Utterson was sitting by his fireside one evening, when he was amazed to have a visit from *Poole*...

What ails you, man? Is the doctor **ill**?

Will you come along with me and see, sir? I think there's been a **crime committed**!

Chapter 8: **THE LAST NIGHT**

It was a wild, cold night in March, with a pale Moon lying on her back.

The wind made talking difficult and reddened their faces with its blast.

Utterson tried hard to get rid of the crushing feeling that something dreadful was about to happen.

The hall was brightly lit up; the fire was stacked high, and beside it the servants were standing close together like a flock of sheep...

Bless God! It's Mr Utterson!

They are all **afraid**, sir.

Please, follow me, and you may learn **why**.

Come as gently as you can, sir. I want you to **hear**, but not **be heard**!

Mr **Utterson**, sir, asking to see you.

Tell him I cannot see anyone.

*"But why had he a **mask** upon his face? Why did he cry out like a **rat**, and **run** from his trusty servant?"*

Your master must be suffering from one of those illnesses which both **torture** and **deform** a man. This explains the **fact** that his voice has changed – and the **mask** – and his **need** to **find** this drug.

That... **thing** was **not** my master, and there's the truth! This was more of a **dwarf!**

I believe in my heart that it was **Edward Hyde** – and that there was **murder** done!

Jekyll! I **must** and **shall** see you! If not by fair means then by foul!

Utterson! For God's sake, have mercy!

That's not Jekyll's voice, it's **Hyde's!**

Down with the door, Poole!

The two men, appalled by the noise of their entry and the stillness that followed, stood back and peered in...

In front of them lay the body of a man, twisted in agony and still *twitching*...

Edward Hyde!

By the crushed bottle in his hand, and the strong smell of kernels... we are looking at the body of a **man who has killed himself!**

Nowhere was there any trace of Henry Jekyll, dead or alive.

I must go home and read these documents in peace. But I shall be back before midnight, Poole...

When we shall send for the **police!**

See now...!

"He reeled, staggered, **staring** with blood-shot eyes, **gasping** with open mouth –"

"He seemed to **swell**, and his face began to **melt** and **change**..."

34

Chapter 10:
HENRY JEKYLL'S FULL STATEMENT OF THE CASE

*I was born to a large **fortune**. Moreover I was a good-looking man and hard-working by nature. Fame and honour should have come easily to me.*

*Indeed, the **worst** of my **faults** was that I too much enjoyed the pleasures of life. This was hard to match up with my great desire to carry my head high.*

*Hence I **hid** these **pleasures**, only to discover in my later years that I had become committed to a double **life**...*

*My **studies** shed a strong light on the scientific reason for this split personality. – With every day I drew nearer to the truth –*

*That man is **not** truly **one**, but truly **two**.*

*If these elements could be split into two **separate beings**, the **unjust** could go his way, no longer bothered by the **shame** his more decent twin would feel...*
*And the **just** could carry on with those good things which he enjoyed doing, no longer risking **disgrace** through his evil twin.*

*I managed to mix a **drug** by which the powers of my spirit would lose their influence over my body. Late one fateful night I drank it down...*

This was followed by racking pain: a **grinding** in the **bones**, deadly **retching** and a **horror** of the **spirit**...

I felt **younger, lighter, happier**. And I knew myself to be more **wicked**—tenfold more wicked!

These agonies swiftly **left me**, and I came to myself as if out of a great sickness.

All human beings are **a mixture** of good and evil. Edward Hyde, alone in the ranks of mankind, was **pure evil!**

If I had tried this out in a more **noble** frame of mind, I would have come forth an **angel** from these agonies instead of a **devil**. But now I had but to drink the drug to take on, like a thick cloak, the **body** of Edward Hyde!

The **pleasures** which I quickly went to find in my new disguise were **beneath me**; and in the hands of Hyde they soon began to turn towards the **horrific**...

Two months before the murder of Danvers Carew, I woke in bed with an odd feeling. I had gone to **sleep** as **Henry Jekyll**...

I was slowly losing contact with my original and better self. So I said goodbye to my secret pleasures, and for **two months** I lived only as Henry Jekyll...

But I woke up as **Edward Hyde**!

The longing for those pleasures began to torture me. Hyde was struggling to gain **freedom**. At last, in an hour of moral weakness, I again mixed the drug...

My devil had been **caged**; he came out **roaring**. I mangled Carew's unresisting body, feeling **delight** at every blow...

I fled from the scene, trembling but happy, my **lust** for **evil** fulfilled and wanting more...

38

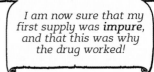

I became weak in both body and mind...
And the powers of Hyde seemed to **grow** with the **sickness** of Jekyll.

I might have been punished like this for years, but for the final disaster which has now hit me: supplies of the drug have run low. I sent out Poole for more – but it no longer had the same effect.

I am now sure that my first supply was **impure**, and that this was why the drug worked!

I am finishing writing this just after having taken the **last** of the **old powders**. This, then, is the last time that **Henry Jekyll** can think his own thoughts, or see his own face...

Doom is closing in on us. Half an hour from now, when I shall again and for ever become the hated Hyde, I know I shall sit **shuddering** and **weeping** in my chair...

Will Hyde **be hanged for murder**? Or will he be brave enough to **release himself** at the last moment?

Here then, as I lay down the pen, and then seal up my confession, I bring the life of that unhappy Henry Jekyll to an end.

The End

40

Robert Louis Stevenson

(1850–1894)

Robert Louis Stevenson was born in Edinburgh in 1850. He studied law at Edinburgh University but by the time he reached his twenties he knew that his real passion was writing.

Stevenson suffered all his life from a serious lung disease, and he travelled constantly in search of a climate that would help him get better. Despite his worsening health he continued to write as much as he could.

In fact, he produced much of his best-known and best-loved work during his years of travel. He had great success with a novel, *Treasure Island* (1883) which became very popular.

In 1886 he wrote *Kidnapped. Kidnapped* became a great favourite and was quickly established as a classic. In 1885 he published a dark thriller about the two sides of human nature and the struggle between good and evil – *Strange Case of Dr Jekyll and Mr Hyde* (1886).

This book, on which this graphic novel is based, established him as a great writer. The story is said to have been written in three days. It is also said that Stevenson threw this first version into the fire and started it again. In a further three days' time he had created the story.

Some say Stevenson created some of the best stories in the English language.

Illustration courtesy Illustrated London News

Alan Grant

Alan Grant is an internationally admired writer of graphic novels and comic strips who has been writing for that industry for nearly 30 years. He always had a love of comics, even as a child, learning to read on his granny's knee with the help of *The Beano* and *The Dandy*.

Alan worked for DC Thomson, the Scottish publisher of those titles, in 1967, where he met his future *Judge Dredd* collaborator John Wagner. In 1979, John Wagner asked him to write his first story for a UK comic called *Starlord* and he finally got to do his dream job, working for comic books like those he read as a teenager.

Alan has written for the world-famous *2000AD* and DC Comics and has worked on many graphic novels including *Judge Dredd*, *Doomlord*, *Legends of the Dark Knight*, *Strontium Dog* and *Joe Soap Private Eye*.

Grant's involvement with *Judge Dredd* has lasted over 25 years and together with John Wagner he created hundreds of stories for what became *2000AD*'s most popular strip.

In 2007, commissioned by Edinburgh UNESCO City of Literature Trust, he started on his first adaptation of a classic novel, creating with artist Cam Kennedy a highly acclaimed graphic novel version of Robert Louis Stevenson's *Kidnapped*. Alan lives in Moniaive in Dumfries and Galloway with his wife, where they organise the yearly Moniaive Comics Festival.

Photograph: Copyright Ian MacNicol.

Cam Kennedy

Cam Kennedy has been working in the comics industry since 1967 and is one of the most respected artists in the business. In 1978, after working as fine artist in France, Kennedy returned to Scotland to work on comics. He sent some drawings to *Battle* comic and was asked to work on *Fighting Mann*. *2000AD* noticed his work on *Battle*, liked it and approached him to work on their strip *Rogue Trooper*.

Soon after this he got the opportunity to work on what would become, arguably, his most famous strip – *Judge Dredd*. He is also well known for his work on The VCs, also for *2000AD*.

Over the years Cam has worked with all the major American publishers, his first American job being for DC Comics – and has worked on many graphic novels and comics including *Star Wars: Dark Empire*, *Daredevil*, *Punisher* and *Batman*.

Cam has been working, on-and-off, with Alan Grant for around 30 years, from his first days on *Judge Dredd* to their present work with Waverley Books.

In 2007 Cam's artwork for the *Kidnapped* graphic novel, commissioned by Edinburgh UNESCO City of Literature Trust as part of their One Book–One Edinburgh campaign, was highly acclaimed and is now to be found in the National Library of Scotland. He joins Alan Grant and Waverley Books once again to create *Strange Case of Dr Jekyll and Mr Hyde*.

Cam lives and works in Orkney where he has stayed for 27 years and claims every time he tries to leave the place the weather is too bad to make the crossing.

Photograph: Copyright Ian MacNicol.

First published 2008 by Barrington Stoke Ltd,
18 Walker Street, Edinburgh EH3 7LP,
by arrangement with Waverley Books Ltd.

www.barringtonstoke.co.uk

Robert Louis Stevenson's *Strange Case of Dr Jekyll and Mr Hyde* – The
Graphic Novel

Adapted Text © 2008 Alan Grant

Illustrations © 2008 Cam Kennedy

ISBN : 978-1-84299-568-6

Scanning by Castle Quoy Graphics & Design, Stromness, Orkney KW16 3AW
Colourist – Jamie Grant, Hope Street Studios, Glasgow G2 6AB
Letterer – Jamie Grant with Niall Connolly

Photographs of Cam Kenned nt © Ian MacNicol

Printed and bound in Graf, Poland